THE WORLD OF
PETER RABBIT™
TREASURY

Fun to Read and Do

With

Stories and Puzzles

From the authorized animated series based on
the original tales by
BEATRIX POTTER™

Bloomsbury Books
in association with Frederick Warne

BLOOMSBURY BOOKS
IN ASSOCIATION WITH FREDERICK WARNE

Published by the Penguin Group
Penguin Books Ltd, 27 Wrights Lane, London W8 5TZ, England
Penguin Books USA Inc., 375 Hudson Street, New York, N.Y. 10014, USA
Penguin Books Australia Ltd, Ringwood, Victoria, Australia
Penguin Books Canada Ltd, 10 Alcorn Avenue, Toronto, Ontario, Canada M4V 3B2
Penguin Books (N.Z.) Ltd, 182-190 Wairau Road, Auckland 10, New Zealand

Penguin Books Ltd, Registered Offices: Harmondsworth, Middlesex, England

Bloomsbury Books, an imprint of the Godfrey Cave Group, 42 Bloomsbury Street, London WC1B 3QJ

This edition first published 1994
1 3 5 7 9 10 8 6 4 2

ISBN 1 85471 389 2

Printed and bound in Great Britain by
BPCC Hazell Books Ltd
Member of BPCC Ltd

£1-50

2.00

CONTENTS

WELCOME TO
THE WORLD OF PETER RABBIT™
TREASURY

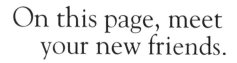

On this page, meet your new friends.

This is Peter Rabbit. He's a very *naughty* rabbit. He's always getting into trouble. You can read about his adventures on page 12.

This is Tom Kitten. He's *always* getting into mischief. You'll be reading about his exploits later – just make sure *you* don't end up in a roly-poly pudding!

Meet Samuel Whiskers and his wife, Anna Maria. These two wicked rats cause poor Mrs Tabitha Twitchit a lot of worry – but are they sorry? Not at all!

What a worry it is, being the mother of three naughty little kittens. Poor Mrs Tabitha Twitchit! Find out how she used to lose her kittens continually, in the story on page 46.

This is old Mrs Rabbit with her daughters Flopsy, Mopsy and Cotton-tail, who are good little bunnies. Peter is nowhere to be seen, of course; he's away in Mr McGregor's garden.

Look at Tom Kitten, Mittens and Moppet playing together. They look sweet and good, don't they? Well, as you'll find out later - they're not!

Peter climbed upon a wheel-barrow and peeped over. The first thing he saw was Mr McGregor hoeing onions. His back was turned towards Peter, and beyond him was the gate! Peter started running as fast as he could go.

PETER RABBIT'S STORY

Once upon a time there were four little rabbits, and their names were Flopsy, Mopsy, Cotton-tail and Peter. They lived with their mother in a sandbank, underneath the root of a very big fir-tree.

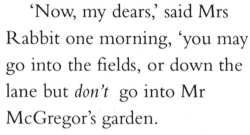

'Now, my dears,' said Mrs Rabbit one morning, 'you may go into the fields, or down the lane but *don't* go into Mr McGregor's garden.

'Run along now and don't get into mischief. I am going out.'

Then old Mrs Rabbit took a basket and her umbrella and went through the wood to the baker.

'Now then, a loaf of brown bread and, let me see, five currant buns,' she said.

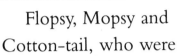

Flopsy, Mopsy and Cotton-tail, who were good little bunnies, went down the lane to gather blackberries. But Peter, who was very naughty, ran straight away to Mr McGregor's garden, and squeezed under the gate!

First he ate some lettuces and some French beans. And then he ate some radishes. 'Ooh! My favourite,' said Peter, happily.

Then, feeling rather sick, he went to look for some parsley. But whom do you think he should meet round the end of a cucumber frame?

'Oh help!' gasped Peter.
'It's Mr McGregor!'

Mr McGregor jumped up and ran after Peter, shouting 'Stop, thief!'

Peter was most dreadfully frightened. He rushed all over the garden, for he had forgotten the way back to the gate. He lost one of his shoes among the cabbages, and the other shoe amongst the potatoes.

Without his shoes, Peter ran on four legs and went faster. He might have got away if he had not got caught up in a gooseberry net.

Peter shed big tears, but his sobs were overheard by some friendly sparrows, who flew to him in great excitement.

'Hurry, Peter, hurry,' urged the sparrows. 'Mr McGregor's coming! Quick, you *must* keep trying.'

Mr McGregor came up with a sieve, which he intended to pop over Peter, but Peter wriggled out just in time, leaving his jacket behind him. He rushed into the toolshed.

Peter jumped into a watering can, and held his breath.

Mr McGregor was quite sure that Peter was somewhere in the tool-shed, perhaps hidden underneath a flower-pot.

'Come on oot, ye wee beastie - I know you're here somewhere,' he muttered.

Then Peter sneezed, 'Kertyshoo!' and Mr McGregor was after him in no time.

Peter sat down to rest; he was out of breath and trembling with fright. He was lost.

He found a door in a wall; but it was locked, and there was no room for a fat little rabbit to squeeze underneath. He saw a little old

mouse carrying peas to her family.

'If you please, Ma'am, could you tell me the way to the gate?' he asked.

She had such a large pea in her mouth that she could not answer.

'Mmmm,' was all she could mumble.

Peter began to cry.

Presently, Peter came to a pond where a white cat was sitting. Peter thought it best to go away without speaking to her; his cousin Benjamin had warned him about cats! And then Peter saw the gate. He ran as fast as he could, slipped under the gate, and was safe at last in the wood.

He ran all the way home.

'Where have you been?' asked Peter's mother. 'And where are your clothes? That is the second little jacket and pair of shoes you've lost in a fortnight.'

Peter was not very well during the evening. Mrs Rabbit put him to bed and gave him a dose of camomile tea.

But Flopsy, Mopsy and Cotton-tail had bread and milk and blackberries for supper.

17

When Peter escaped from Mr McGregor's garden, he never stopped running or looked behind him till he got home to the big fir-tree. He was so tired that he flopped down upon the nice soft sand on the floor of the rabbit-hole and shut his eyes.

1 ROUND AND ROUND THE GARDEN

Here is a maze, showing Peter Rabbit in Mr McGregor's garden. Can you find a clear path for Peter to follow, through the garden to the gate at the other side?

Then, fill in the missing letters to complete the word puzzle. It shows a bird that Peter met in the garden, and some things that he lost there as he was trying to escape.

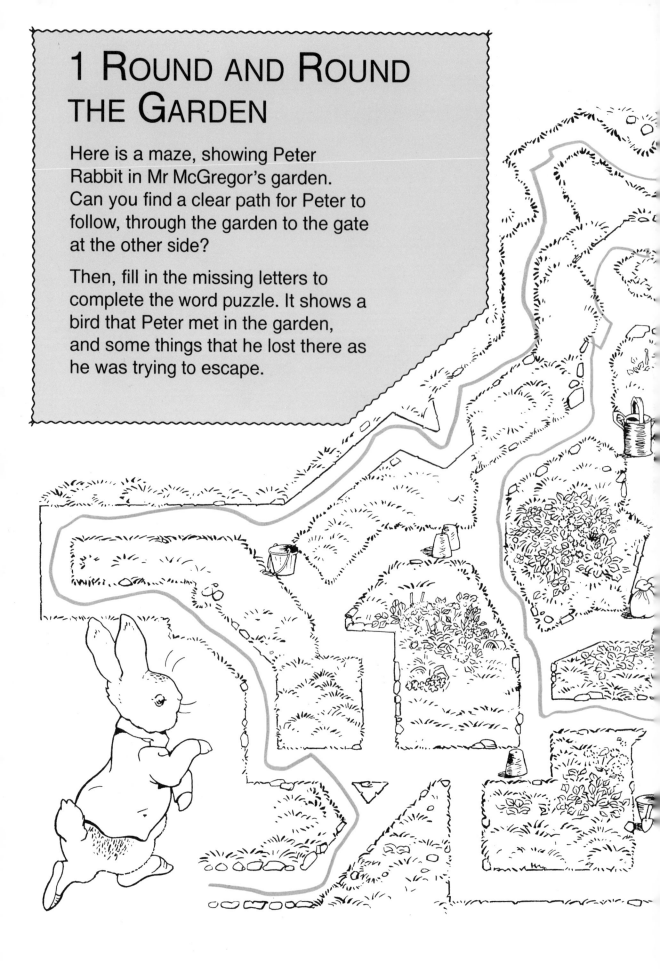

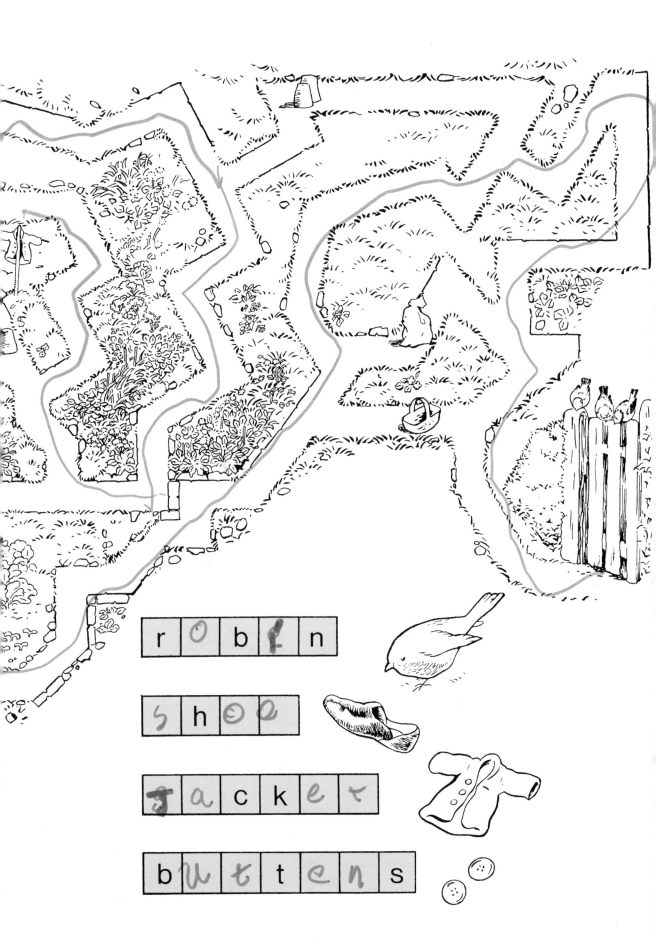

r o b i n

s h o e

j a c k e r

b u t t e n s

JOIN THE DOTS

Knock, knock! Who's there?

Join the dots to finish off this picture, following the numbers. Now why not paint or colour the scene?

WHERE IS PETER?

Where is Peter? He's eating radishes in Mr McGregor's garden, of course! Paint or colour this picture from *The Tale of Peter Rabbit*. Be careful - remember radishes are not the same colour as carrots!

When Peter Rabbit escaped from the garden leaving his clothes behind him, Mr McGregor hung up the little jacket and the shoes for a scare-crow to frighten the birds. Later, Peter and his cousin Benjamin Bunny decided to retrieve the clothes and had a great adventure...but that's another story.

2 THE GREAT ESCAPE

This crossword puzzle tells the story of Peter's adventures in Mr McGregor's garden. Don't forget, you can always look at the answers on page 60 if you get stuck filling in the letters.

CLUES

1	*down*	Peter squeezes under the ___.
1	*across*	In the garden, he ___ some radishes.
2	*down*	He eats so much, he feels rather ___.
2	*across*	Then suddenly, Mr _____ appears!
3	*down*	Peter ___ away as fast as he can.
3	*across*	He loses a ___ among the cabbages.
4	*down*	Mr McGregor tries to catch Peter with a sieve, but he ___ out just in time.

								5		
	t			i			c		n	
								s		
						6		t		
					l					
					b					
			7		l		p			

4   *across*   Peter jumps into a _____ (8,3) to hide.

5   *down*   Mr McGregor hears him sneeze, and ____ him again.

6   *across*   Peter finds one of the ____ watching some goldfish.

6   *down*   To see the way out, he ____ up on a wheelbarrow.

7   *across*   Peter ____ underneath the gate, and he's free!

27

TOM KITTEN'S STORY

Once upon a time there were three little kittens and their names were Mittens, Tom Kitten and Moppet.

They had dear little coats of their own; and they tumbled about the door-step and played in the dust.

'I do wish Mrs Twitchit would keep her kittens in order,' quacked Jemima Puddle-duck.

One day their mother,

Mrs Tabitha Twitchit, expected friends to tea, so she fetched the kittens indoors to wash and dress them before the fine company arrived.

Mrs Tabitha Twitchit dressed Moppet and Mittens in clean pinafores and tuckers; then she took all sorts of elegant uncomfortable clothes out of a chest of drawers, to dress up her son Thomas.

'Goodness me, Tom, I had not realised quite how you have grown. Oh dear, oh dear!' sighed Mrs Tabitha Twitchit. 'We'll just have to see what we can do.'

'Now, you must walk on your hind legs and keep away from the dirty ash-pit. And from the pigstye - oh, and the Puddle-ducks,' said Mrs Tabitha Twitchit.

Then she let the kittens out to play in the garden while she got the tea ready.

'Ooh, let's climb up the rockery and sit on the garden wall,' suggested Moppet.

They went up with a skip and a jump. Moppet's white tucker fell down into the road. 'Never mind,' she said, 'we can fetch it later. Now, where's Tom?'

'Come along, Tom, hurry yourself up.'

Tom was all in pieces when he reached the top of the wall; his hat fell off and the rest of his buttons burst.

While Moppet and Mittens tried to pull him together, there was a pit pat paddle-pat! and three Puddle-ducks came along the road, marching one behind the other - pit pat paddle pat! pit pat waddle pat!

The ducks stopped and stared up at the kittens. Then Rebeccah and Jemima Puddle-duck, picked up the hat and tucker and put them on.

'Rather fetching, don't you agree, Jemima?' asked Rebeccah as she tried on the hat.

Mittens laughed so much she fell off the wall. Moppet and Tom followed her down.

'Come, Mr Drake Puddle-duck,' said Moppet. 'Come and help me to dress Tom. Come and button him up.'

But Mr Drake put Tom's clothes on himself. They fitted him even worse than Tom Kitten.

'It's a very fine morning,' he said. And he and Jemima and Rebeccah Puddle-duck set off up the road, keeping step - pit pat, paddle pat! pit pat, waddle pat!

Then Mrs Tabitha Twitchit came down the garden and found her kittens on the wall with no clothes on.

She pulled them off the wall, smacked them, and took them back to the house.

'My friends will arrive in a moment,' she said, 'and you are not fit to be seen – I am affronted.'

'Straight to your room and not one sound do I wish to hear,' she ordered.

I'm afraid to say Mrs Tabitha Twitchit told her friends that the kittens were in bed with measles, which was not true.

'Dear, dear. What a shame. The poor little souls,' exclaimed Henrietta.

But the kittens were not in bed; not in the least.

Somehow there were some very extraordinary noises over-head, which disturbed the dignity and repose of the tea party.

'You did say they were poorly, didn't you, Tabitha dear?' asked Cousin Ribby.

As for the Puddle-ducks, they went into a pond.

The clothes all came off directly, because there were no buttons. And Mr Drake Puddle-duck, and Jemima and Rebeccah, have been looking for them ever since.

When Mrs Tabitha Twitchit expected friends to tea, she fetched her kittens indoors, to wash and dress them. First she scrubbed their faces. Then she brushed their fur, then she combed their tails and whiskers.

FIND THE BUTTONS

Tom Kitten and his sisters Mittens and Moppet are playing
in the garden in their best clothes. Unfortunately, all
the buttons have burst off, and they won't stay dressed for
long. Can you find all the missing buttons?
Each kitten had three when they started out. Then, why
not paint or colour the scene?

NAUGHTY KITTENS!
On no! They're in trouble again! Paint or colour
this picture of the naughty kittens from
The Tale of Tom Kitten.

Tom Kitten was quite unable to jump when walking upon his hind legs in trousers. He came up by degrees, shedding buttons right and left. He was all in pieces when he reached the top of the wall!

3 Big Bad Crossword

How well do you know the Beatrix Potter stories?
Try this crossword, and if you get stuck, you'll find the answers on page 60. Once you've tried this crossword, you might also like to read the stories again. There's a complete list of the famous Peter Rabbit Books on page 61.

CLUES

Down

1 What is the name of Goody Tiptoes's husband? *(5,7)*
2 Tom Kitten's youngest sister, playing in the garden.
3 *down and 3 across* Who is Tom Kitten's mother?
4 What is the name of Pickles's fellow shopkeeper?
5 This is the carpenter who rescued Tom Kitten. *(4,6)*
6 The hero of this book, who squeezed under the gate in Mr McGregor's garden. *(5,6)*
7 Mrs ________ is the washerwoman pegging out her laundry.
8 The gentleman rat who captured Tom Kitten. *(6,8)*
9 Who invited Duchess to a tea party?
10 *down and 8 across* Peter Rabbit's cousin, who went into the garden with him to take vegetables.

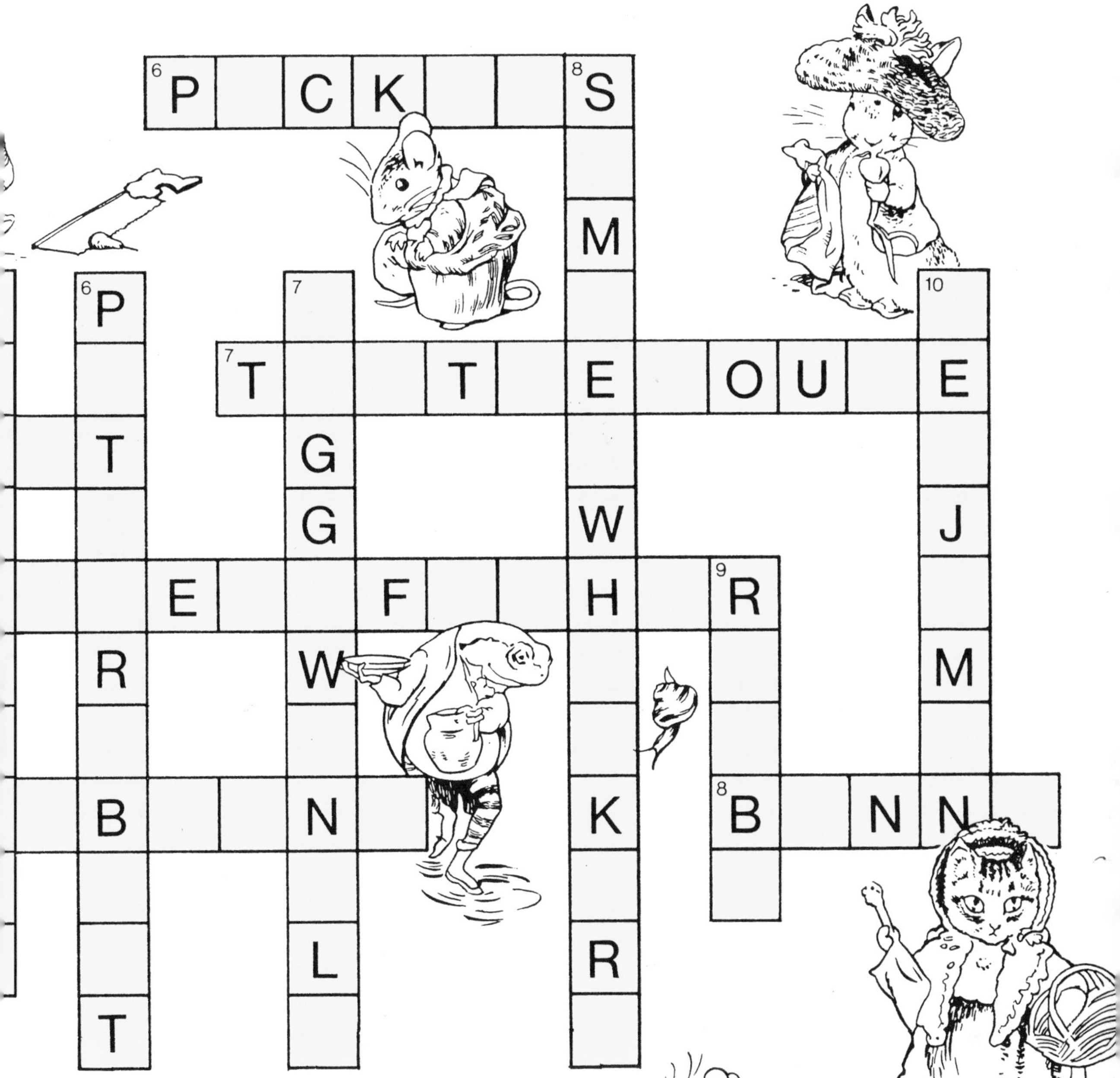

Across

1 Who was made into a roly-poly pudding by Samuel Whiskers and Anna Maria? *(3,6)*

2 What is the name of Tom Kitten's middle sister?

3 *See 3 down*

4 This little pig does *not* want to go to market! *(7,5)*

5 Who has a boat made out of a lily leaf? *(6,6)*

6 Who keeps a shop with Ginger?

7 Mrs _________ likes to keep her home clean and tidy.

8 *See 10 down*

TOM SHEDS HIS BUTTONS

Poor Tom! He can't seem to keep his clothes neat and tidy.
In fact, he can't seem to keep his clothes at all! Paint or colour this
picture from *The Tale of Tom Kitten*. Look at pages 38 and 39 to
help you choose your colours.

JOIN THE DOTS
Bunnies at the Window

Three of the Flopsy Bunnies are listening at the window to Mr and Mrs McGregor quarrelling in the kitchen. Join up the dots to finish off the picture, following the numbers, and then why not paint or colour the scene?

43

When Jemima Puddle-duck tried on her hat, Mittens laughed so much that she fell off the wall!

SAMUEL WHISKERS' STORY

Once upon a time there was an old cat, called Mrs Tabitha Twitchit, who was an anxious parent.

She used to lose her kittens continually, and whenever they were lost they were in mischief.

'And there you stay my two young rascals, until my baking is finished,' said Mrs Tabitha Twitchit to Moppet and Mittens as she shut them in a cupboard.

But she could not find Tom.

Tom Kitten did not want to be shut up in a cupboard. He looked about for a convenient place to hide and fixed upon the chimney.

Inside the chimney, Tom coughed and choked with the smoke. He decided to climb right to the top.

'I cannot go back. If I slipped I might fall in the fire and singe my beautiful tail and my little blue jacket,' he said.

Mrs Tabitha Twitchit was upstairs looking for Tom. As Moppet and Mittens pushed the cupboard door open, somebody knocked at the door.

'Tabitha! Are you at home, Tabitha?'

'Oh, come in Cousin Ribby. I'm in sad trouble. I've lost my dear son Thomas. I'm afraid the rats have got him,' sobbed Mrs Tabitha Twitchit.

'And now Moppet and Mittens are gone too. What it is to have an unruly family,' she wailed.

'Well Cousin, we shan't find any of them standing here,' said Cousin Ribby firmly. 'I'm not afraid of rats. I'll help you find Tom – and whip him too. Now – just where would a naughty little kitten hide?'

Tom Kitten was getting very frightened. It was confusing in the dark, and he felt quite lost.

He began to run when all at once he fell head over heels down a hole and landed on a heap of very dirty rags.

Opposite to him – as far away as he could sit – was an enormous rat.

'What do you mean by tumbling into my bed all covered with smuts?' said the rat (whose name was Samuel Whiskers).

'Please, sir, the chimney wants sweeping,' said poor Tom Kitten.

'Anna Maria! Anna Maria!' Samuel Whiskers called. An old woman rat poked her head round a rafter.

She rushed upon Tom Kitten and before he knew what was happening, he was rolled up in a bundle, and tied with string in very hard knots.

'Anna Maria,' said the old man rat. 'Anna Maria, make me a kitten dumpling roly-poly pudding for my dinner.'

And he licked his lips.

'Hmmm,' she considered. 'It requires dough and a pat of butter and a rolling-pin.'

The two rats consulted together for a few minutes and then went away.

Samuel Whiskers went to the

dairy to get the butter. He made a second
journey for the rolling-pin.

Anna Maria went to the kitchen to steal the
dough.

Presently the rats came back and set to work
to make Tom Kitten into a dumpling.

Meanwhile, Ribby found Moppet hiding in
a flour barrel.

'Oh Mother, Mother! There's been an old woman rat in the kitchen
and she's stolen some of the dough,' cried the kitten.

Then Mittens, who had been found hiding in a jar, cried out;
'There's been an old man rat in the dairy - a dreadful 'normous big rat,
Mother. He's stolen a pat of butter and a rolling-pin.'

'Oh my poor son, Thomas,'
exclaimed Tabitha, wringing her
paws.

Ribby and Mrs Tabitha
Twitchit rushed upstairs. There
was a roly-poly noise going on
quite distinctly under the attic
floor.

'This is serious, Cousin
Tabitha,' said Ribby. 'We must
send for John Joiner at once,
with a saw.'

'I do not think... I do *not* think it will be a good pudding,' said Samuel Whiskers looking at Tom Kitten. 'It smells sooty.'

Anna Maria was about to argue the point when they heard noises up above - the rasping noise of a saw; and the noise of a little dog, scratching and yelping.

'We are discovered and interrupted, Anna Maria. Let us collect our property (and other people's) and depart at once.'

Then Samuel Whiskers and Anna Maria found a wheelbarrow belonging to Miss Potter which they borrowed and hastily filled with a quantity of bundles.

'There may just have been room for the pudding,' said Samuel Whiskers wistfully.

Anna Maria and Samuel Whiskers made their way to Farmer Potatoes' hay barn and hauled their parcels with a bit of string to the top of the hay mow.

'Have you, er, given any thought to, er, supper?' Samuel Whiskers asked.

The cat family quickly recovered. The dumpling was peeled off Tom Kitten and made separately into a pudding, with currants in it to hide the smuts.

After that there were no more rats for a long time at Mrs Tabitha Twitchit's.

Samuel Whiskers and Anna Maria set to work to make Tom Kitten into a dumpling. 'Will not the string be very indigestible, Anna Maria?" inquired Samuel Whiskers. "No, no, no. It's of no consequence,' she replied before turning to Tom. 'I do wish you would stop moving your head about. It disarranges the dough so.'

Up the Chimney

Here is a three-part maze, which shows
what happened to Tom Kitten when he climbed
up the chimney and met two rats, Samuel Whiskers
and Anna Maria. First, trace the path Tom took to reach the
rats' room, where he was made into a roly-poly pudding. Then,
see how the carpenter dog, John Joiner, tunnelled down to
rescue him. Finally, find out how the rats themselves escaped.

PAINT A PICTURE

ANNA MARIA 'BORROWS' SOME DOUGH

Anna Maria does not see Moppet hiding, in this picture from
The Tale of Samuel Whiskers. Paint or colour the picture, making
sure that you don't miss Moppet's ears!

4 GARDEN CROSSWORD

Mr McGregor has left all his tools lying about the garden. Answer the clues below to fill in the crossword and find out their names. The picures below should help you too!

CLUES

Down
1 Useful for carrying loads.
2 Fishermen use this too.
3 You can clear away dead leaves with this.
4 *and 6 across* Gardeners need this in summer.

Across
1 A cook will use this too, for getting rid of lumps.
2 More useful than *1* for carrying water.
3 This goes with a knife, for eating.
4 The best thing for weeding, it rhymes with 'slow'.
5 You can plant seeds with this, and root up weeds.
6 This goes with *4 down*, to help thirsty plants.

By the time John Joiner
had got the plank up -
Samuel Whiskers and
Anna Maria had fled.
There was nobody
under the floor except
the rolling-pin and Tom
Kitten in a very dirty
dumpling!

Answers

1 Round and Round the Garden

(missing letters puzzle)
robin; shoe; jacket; buttons

2 The Great Escape

1 *down*	gate
1 *across*	eats
2 *down*	sick
2 *across*	McGregor
3 *down*	runs
3 *across*	shoe
4 *down*	wriggles
4 *across*	watering can
5 *down*	chases
6 *across*	cats
6 *down*	climbs
7 *across*	slips

3 Big Bad Crossword

Down

1 Timmy Tiptoes
2 Moppet
3 *and 3 across* Tabitha Twitchit
4 Ginger
5 John Joiner
6 Peter Rabbit
7 Tiggy-winkle
8 Samuel Whiskers
9 Ribby
10 *and 8 across* Benjamin Bunny

Across

1 Tom Kitten
2 Mittens
3 *see 3 down*
4 Pigling Bland
5 Jeremy Fisher
6 Pickles
7 Tittlemouse
8 *see 10 down*

4 Garden Crossword

Down

1 wheelbarrow
2 net
3 rake
4 *and 6 across* watering can

Across

1 sieve
2 bucket
3 fork
4 hoe
5 trowel
6 *and 4 down* watering can

Here is a complete list of some other Beatrix Potter books you may enjoy:

THE PETER RABBIT BOOKS

1 *The Tale of Peter Rabbit*
2 *The Tale of Squirrel Nutkin*
3 *The Tailor of Gloucester*
4 *The Tale of Benjamin Bunny*
5 *The Tale of Two Bad Mice*
6 *The Tale of Mrs. Tiggy-Winkle*
7 *The Tale of Mr. Jeremy Fisher*
8 *The Tale of Tom Kitten*
9 *The Tale of Jemima Puddle-Duck*
10 *The Tale of The Flopsy Bunnies*
11 *The Tale of Mrs. Tittlemouse*
12 *The Tale of Timmy Tiptoes*
13 *The Tale of Johnny Town-Mouse*
14 *The Tale of Mr. Tod*
15 *The Tale of Pigling Bland*
16 *The Tale of Samuel Whiskers or The Roly-Poly Pudding*
17 *The Tale of The Pie and The Patty-Pan*
18 *The Tale of Ginger and Pickles*
19 *The Tale of Little Pig Robinson*
20 *The Story of A Fierce Bad Rabbit*
21 *The Story of Miss Moppet*
22 *Appley Dapply's Nursery Rhymes*
23 *Cecily Parsley's Nursery Rhymes*